BERMUDA TRIANGLES

When Surfer Sam went to the beach in Bermuda, there were triangles everywhere. How many can you find in this picture?

Illustrated by Barbara Gray

Answer on page 47.

MIRROR, MIRROR

Look closely. Only one of these fun house mirrors shows the real reflection of Winifred Whiffet. Which one is it?

1.

Illustrated by Pat Merrell

DOWN ON THE ANT FARM

After a hard day's work, this little farmer is ready for supper. See if you can tell which path he must follow to get home.

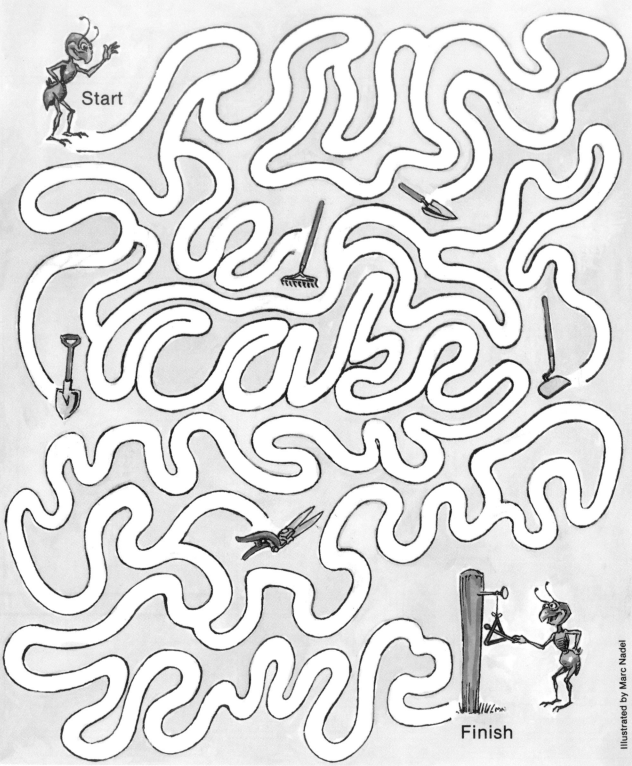

Start

Finish

Illustrated by Marc Nadel

Answer on page 47.

FRUIT SALAD

Nine delicious fruits are hiding in this box of letters. Look up, down, sideways, and diagonally to find them. Some words are backwards. Some letters are used in more than one word. Circle each word that you find. When you finish, there should be three letters left. Those three letters spell a word that means the seed we find inside some fruits.

APPLE	PEAR
DATE	CHERRY
PEACH	ORANGE
BANANA	PRUNE
FIG	

```
O  P  D  A  T  E
Y  R  R  E  H  C
R  U  A  C  P  I
A  N  A  N  A  B
E  E  F  I  G  T
P  A  P  P  L  E
```

Fruit seed: ___ ___ ___

CROSSED WIRES

Who's calling whom? Follow the
telephone cords to find the answers.

Answer on page 47.

3.

4.

8.

7.

Illustrated by Barbara Gray

NAPPING NUMBERS

Neat Nicky, the number nanny, must tuck in the rest of the numbers. Find the right number to nap next in each bed.

A. 1 3 5 7

B. 21 16 11 6

C. 9 11 10 12 11

D. 1 2 4 8

E. 5 15 25 35

F. 4 3 4 3

Illustrated by Barbara Gray

Answer on page 47.

PUZZLE OF THE MONTH

1. Which month has the fewest days?
   _____

2. Which month makes us think of shamrocks and leprechauns?
   _____

3. Which three months begin with the same letter?
   _____

4. During which month does spring begin?
   _____

5. Which month has the fewest letters in its name?
   _____

6. Which one has the most letters in its name?
   _____

7. In which month do we celebrate Mother's Day and Memorial Day?
   _____

8. In which month do we celebrate Father's Day and Flag Day?
   _____

9. Which month has a holiday that is always on a Thursday?
   _____

10. Which month comes after Independence Day and before Labor Day?
    _____

Illustrated by Barbera Gray

Answer on page 47.

THE MYSTERY OF THE CASTLE

Eric and his parents visited a castle in England one summer. Before he went inside, Eric noticed a pattern of unusual markings on the many stones that formed the front wall of the castle. Each marking was made up of two or more connecting lines and one dot. Eric believed that the markings contained a secret message, but he could not figure out how to read it. Later, inside the great hall of the castle, Eric saw something carved in the stone on one of the walls.

Suddenly, Eric understood how to read the message on the front of the castle. He ran outside to see what it said. Can you read the secret message?

Starter Hint: = MY

WHO'S THIS?

Who could this be? Is it a clown? Is it your best friend in a Halloween costume? How about a visitor from Jupiter? The answer is up to you. Use your imagination and finish the picture.

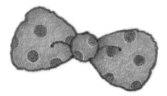

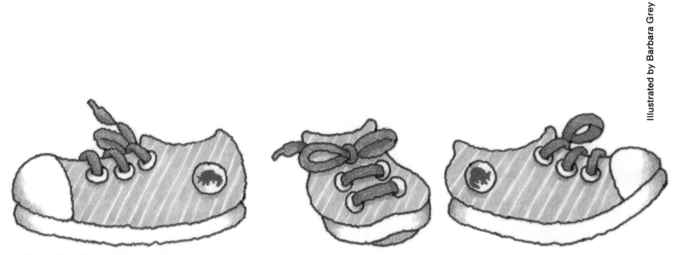

Illustrated by Barbara Grey

LULU'S FIX-IT SHOP

Unscramble these words to make household items. The numbered letters will tell you what Lulu is fixing.

PRETTIERWY
  _ _ _ _ _ _ _ _ _ _
                 1

LISTENOVIE
  _ _ _ _ _ _ _ _ _ _
                  2

ARIH DERRY
  _ _ _ _ _ _ _ _
    3

WHIGANS HEMNICA
  _ _ _ _ _ _ _ _ _ _ _ _ _
      4

HELPNOTEE
  _ _ _ _ _ _ _ _ _
  5

GIRRAFERROTE
  _ _ _ _ _ _ _ _ _ _ _
    6

CAVUMU NACREEL
  _ _ _ _ _ _ _ _ _ _ _ _
                 7

_ _ _ _ _ _ _
1 2 3 4 5 6 7

Answer on page 47.

MATCH THAT HAT

Only two of these hats are exactly alike. Can you find them?

Answer on page 47.

DOT MAGIC

Connect the dots from 1 to 180 to make a picture
of an animal in its home.

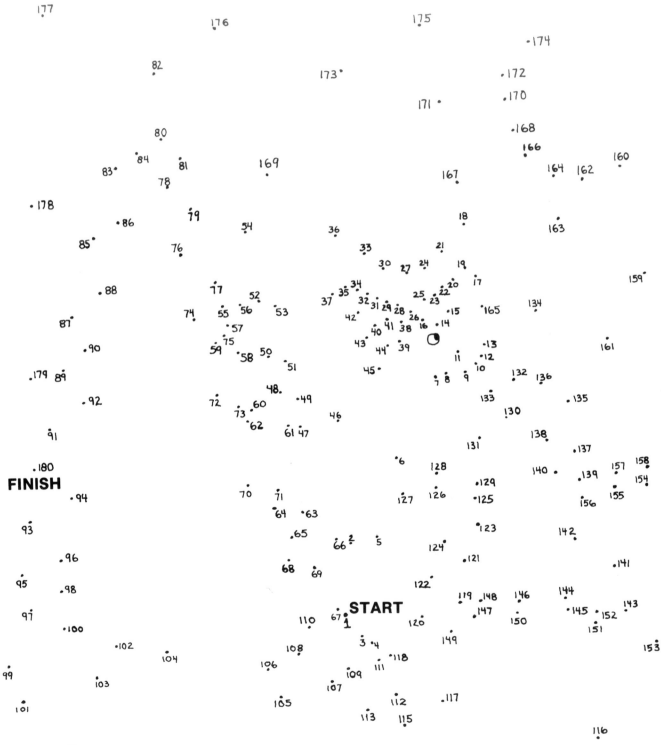

CAMPING OUT

How many things can you find
wrong in this picture?

Illustrated by Holly Kowitt

Coendu

Red Uakari

Ross's Turaco

Takin

Roseate Spoonbill

Heedee

Pangolin

Spatulate-Nosed
Tree Frog

Answer on page 48.

Illustrated by Marc Nadel

INSTANT PICTURE

What's hidden on this page? To find out, fill in every section that contains four dots.

Illustrated by McKenzie/Perrin

Answer on page 48.

GO FLY A KITE!

What kind of paper makes the best kites? Follow the directions below. Then unscramble the leftover letters to find the answer.

1. Cross out the M's and Q's.
2. Cross out the vowels in Column 4.
3. Cross out the letters in Row b that come before H in the alphabet.
4. Cross out the consonants in Row e.
5. Cross out the I's and U's.

	1	2	3	4	5	6
a	M	F	Q	O	I	U
b	D	G	Y	R	E	C
c	M	I	Q	E	M	P
d	Q	U	I	L	U	I
e	W	J	E	A	X	K
f	U	P	M	Q	A	I

_ _ _ _ _ _ _ _ !

Illustrated by Jerry Zimmerman

LOCKER LOGIC

Can you tell which locker belongs to each student? Their last names are posted.

1. Susan and Karen have two classes together.

2. Ricky's team wears helmets but Pam's does not.

3. Karen and Donnie walk home together from marching band practice.

Answer on page 48.

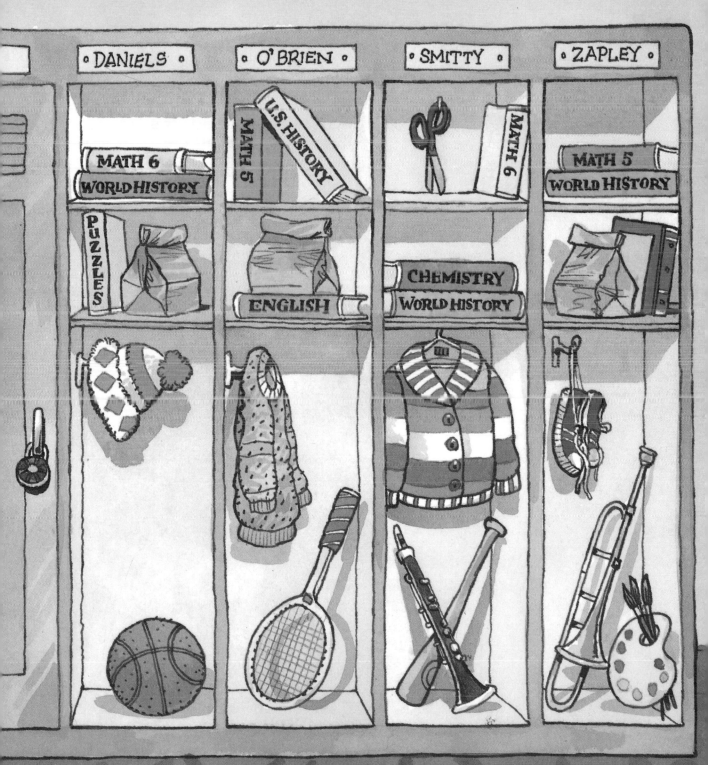

A SLIPPERY RIDDLE

Monkey fruit
In a yellow suit.
Precious bunch
Like pirates' loot.
Fly off balance,
Slip on the heel
From the careless throw
Of a ...

_ _ _ _ _ _

_ _ _ _

Answer on page 48.

PICTURE CROSSWORD

These pictures tell you what words to write in the spaces across ⟶ and down ↓.

Illustrated by Jerry Zimmerman

Answer on page 48.

TWEETERS, PEEPERS, AND QUACKERS

How many of these animal sounds do you know?

1. The sound a kitten makes is . . . **tweet   purr   hiss**
2. To frighten burglars a dog will . . . **roar   bark   cluck**
3. In the morning a rooster will . . . **neigh   crow   jabber**
4. A mother hen will sometimes . . . **cluck   moo   bleat**
5. Her baby chicks follow with a . . . **quack   peep   croak**
6. A horse in a stable might . . . **hiss   neigh   crow**

7. Cows in a barn are likely to . . . **screech honk moo**
8. Bees around flowers will often . . . **growl snort buzz**

9. A duck in a pond says . . . **quack chirp hum**
10. A happy little bird may . . . **bark tweet gurgle**
11. A slinky snake likes to . . . **sing chatter hiss**

12. In the jungle you'd hear a lion . . . **roar gobble squawk**
13. A frog in a pond would . . . **whistle croak cackle**

Answer on page 49.

SQUEAKY'S SNEAKY SNACK

Can you help Squeaky sneak quietly past the napping cats to get to his favorite snack?

START

FINISH

Illustrated by Barbara Gray

Answer on page 49.

MIXED-UP WARM-UPS

Unscramble the words below to find six things that keep you warm. Then match each word to the picture that shows where it is worn.

1. THA

_____

2. CRAFS

_____

3. TOSBO

_____

4. TINSTEM

_____

5. FRAUSMEF

_____

6. GEL SWARREM

_____

A.

B.

C.

D.

E.

F.

Illustrated by Terry Kovalcik

Answer on page 49.

DOT'S DEPARTMENT STORE

What did Alex buy at Dot's Department Store? Connect the dots to find out.

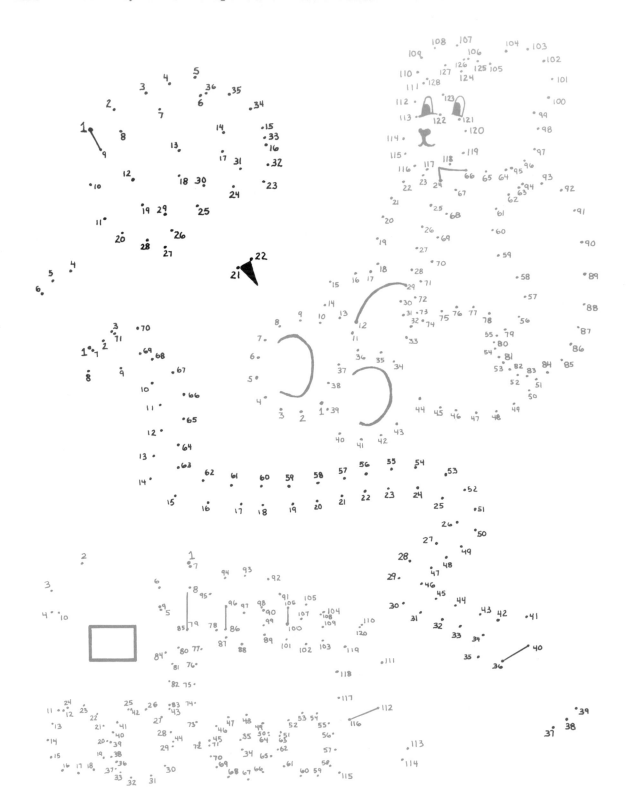

Answer on page 49.

ANIMALS, ANIMALS, ANIMALS

ACROSS

1. Young sheep
4. Australian teddy bear look-alike
7. Fish flipper
8. The hen sat __ __ the eggs.
9. Opposite of down
10. Ball-balancing circus animal
11. Slithering reptile
13. Honey-eater who hibernates
15. Getting older; rhymes with raging
16. A hot drink
17. Three blind mice, see how they __ __ __."
18. A female deer
20. Sick; rhymes with hill
21. Your sound catcher
24. Picnic pest with wings
25. Railroad abbreviation
26. Tortoise's rival
27. Saltwater animals' home

DOWN

1. Jungle king
2. Girl's name; rhymes with banana
3. Sky-colored bird
5. Big monkey
6. Crocodile's cousin
11. Five-pointed beach creature
12. Bald bird
14. What kitten shares with hen
15. Headgear for an elk
16. Striped jungle cats
19. Nighttime hoo-hooter
22. What fare and scare share

Illustrated by Barbara Gray

Answer on page 49.

SEA SIGHTS

These pictures and letters may remind you of things to see at the sea.
The first one is a starfish. Can you tell what the others are?

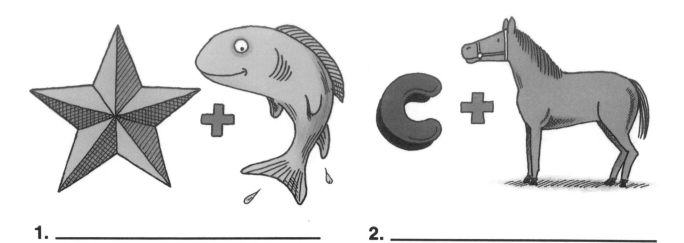

1. _____   2. _____

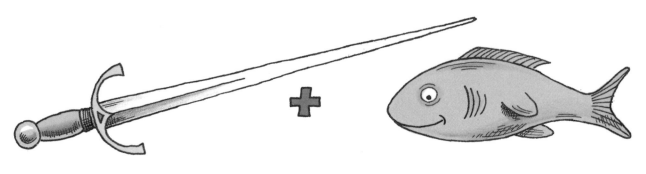

3. _____

4. _____   5. _____

Illustrated by Pat Merrell

Answer on page 49.

TOP IT OFF

Chef Ann Chovie thinks she put exactly the same amount of each topping on every pizza, but she goofed. Which pizza is missing something?

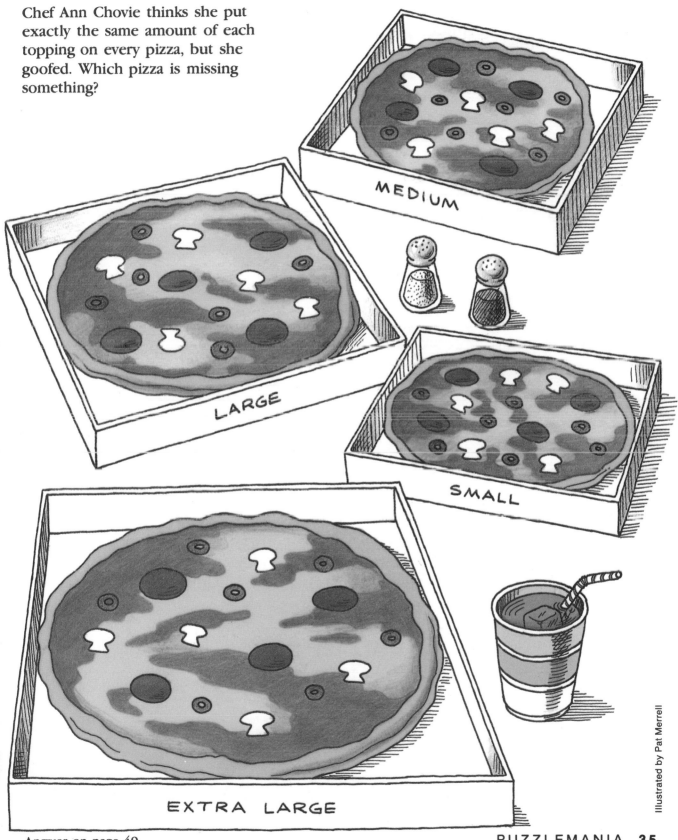

MEDIUM

LARGE

SMALL

EXTRA LARGE

Answer on page 49.

HIDDEN PICTURES

There are at least 12 objects hidden in
this picture. How many can you find?

Illustrated by Carol Sutherby

PUZZLED POET

Dear Puzzler,
Help! I have worked and worked on this poem, but my rhymes don't make sense. Will you please fix the rhyming words?

Thanks,
Puzzled Poet

fly   too   sky   high   do   you   sigh   blue

As I looked upward toward the ___
I wondered with a longing ____,
How things might look from way up ____.
How would it feel if I could ___?

Do you think birds wonder, ___,
As they're soaring in the ____
How it would be if they could __
People things like me and ___?

Illustrated by Judith Hunt

Answer on page 49.

SLICK SHIPPING COMPANY

The Slick Shippers slipped one by again. No one can tell what the boxes contain, unless he or she knows the secret code. Can you find the box they slipped into the museum's order by mistake?

Secret Shipping Code:

A = O		**N** = G
B = F		**O** = A
C = K		**P** = S
D = M		**Q** = J
E = Y		**R** = L
F = B		**S** = P
G = N		**T** = H
H = T		**U** = I
I = U		**V** = X
J = Q		**W** = Z
K = C		**X** = V
L = R		**Y** = E
M = D		**Z** = W

MUSEUM "BAPPUR" ORDER

1. HLUKYLOHASP _____

2. ORRAPOILIP _____

3. PHYNAPOILIP _____

4. HELOGGAPOILIP _____

5. FLAGHAPOILIP _____

6. MUSRAMAKIP _____

7. FULHTMOE KOCY _____

8. OGCERAPOILIP _____

Illustrated by Dennis Panek

PLAY BALL!

These twenty baseball words are hidden in the diamond at right. Look up, down, across, diagonally, and backward. Some letters are used in more than one word. When you find a word, circle it and cross it off the list.

BALL	CATCHER	MITT	SECOND
BASEBALL	FIELDER	OUT	SHORTSTOP
BASEMAN	FIRST	PITCHER	STRIKE
BAT	FOUL	POPUP	THIRD
BATTER	HOME	SAFE	UMPIRE

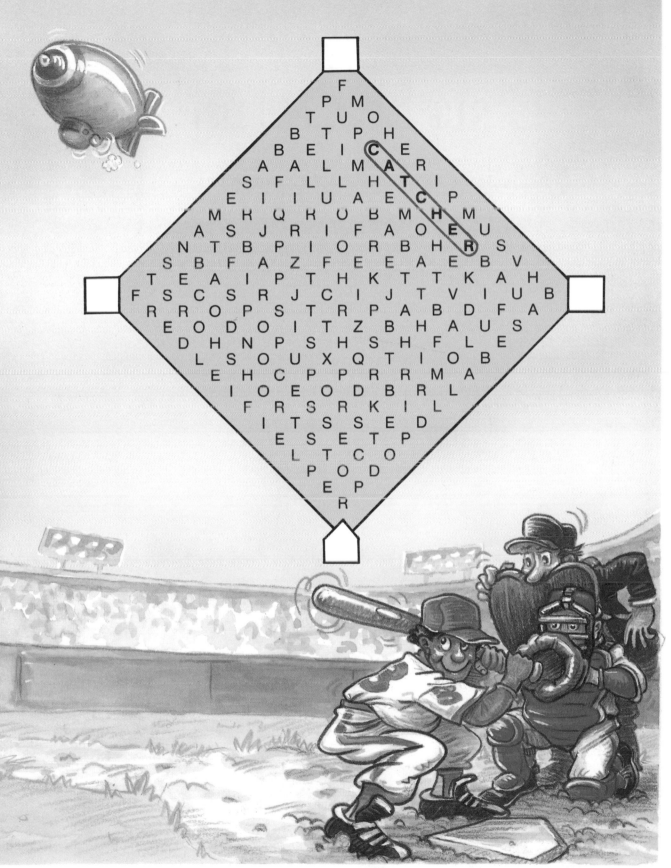

STOP, LOOK, AND LIST

Under each category list one thing that begins with each letter. For example, one food that begins with R is RAISIN. See if you can name another.

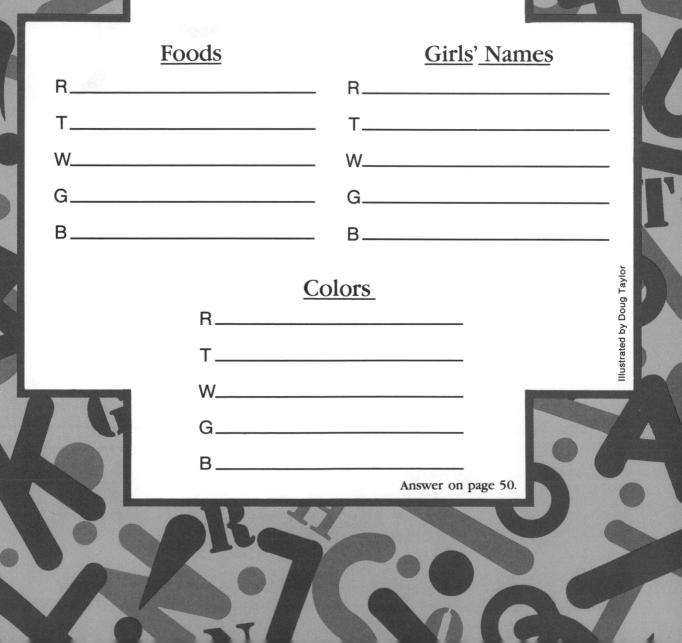

Foods

R_____

T_____

W_____

G_____

B_____

Girls' Names

R_____

T_____

W_____

G_____

B_____

Colors

R_____

T_____

W_____

G_____

B_____

Illustrated by Doug Taylor

Answer on page 50.

THE POTTER'S GIFT

Clay Wheelie, the famous potter, made a gift for his friend. Number the pictures to show what Clay did first, second, and so on.

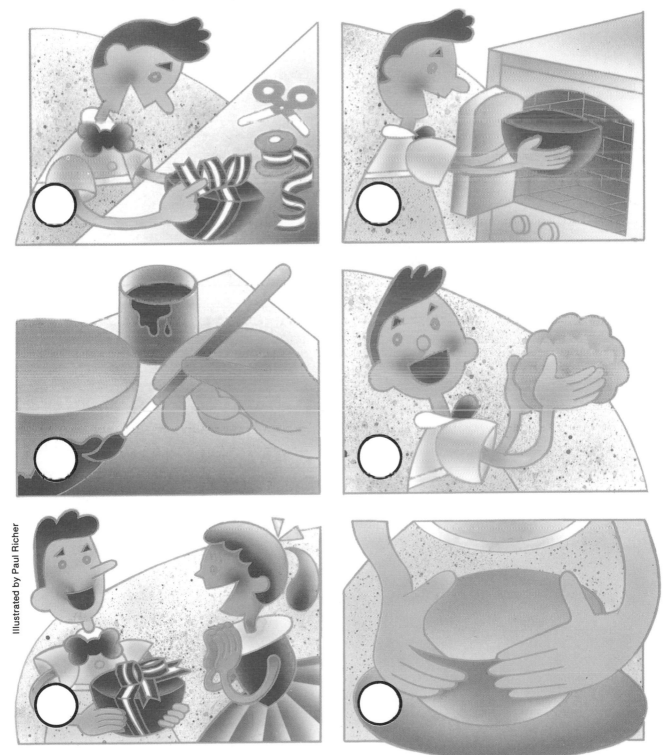

Illustrated by Paul Richer

Answer on page 50.

PICNIC MEMORIES

Every year the Munchly family gathers for a picnic. Uncle Mitch always takes a picture so he can remember the fun everyone had.

Take a good look at Uncle Mitch's picture. Try to remember everything you see. Then turn the page and see if you can answer some questions about the picnic.

DON'T READ THIS UNTIL YOU HAVE LOOKED AT "Picnic Memories—Part 1" ON PAGES 44-45.

PICNIC MEMORIES
Part 2

Can you answer these questions about the Munchly family picnic?

1. What was cooking on the grill?
2. How many people were playing horseshoes?
3. How many girls were playing volleyball?
4. What were the twins' names?
5. What were Marty and Aunt Millie playing at the table?
6. How many babies were at the picnic?
7. Where was Munchkin, the family cat?
8. What was cousin Mark balancing on his head?
9. How many years have the Munchlys held their picnic?
10. What did Mrs. Munchly find in the cooler?

Answer on page 50.

DOWNTOWN U.S.A.

Look at the clues and fill in the names of the cities. When you are finished, the letters in the yellow spaces will spell a city that also was the name of a president.

Illustrated by Jerry Zimmerman

Liberty Bell city
Largest city in Illinois
Florida Disney city
Ohio capital
California "City of Angels"
Georgia Capital
Colorado "Mile High" city

Answer on page 50.

ANSWERS

COVER

ladder, lady, ladybug, lake, lamb, lantern, laughing, leash, leaves, legs, lemon, lemonade, leopard, letter, lettuce, license plate, licorice, lights, lighthouse, lightning, lima bean, limes, Lincoln, lines, links, lion, lips, lizard, llama, lobster, lock, log, lollipops, Louisiana

BERMUDA TRIANGLES (page 3)

95

MIRROR, MIRROR (page 4)

3

DOWN ON THE ANT FARM (page 6)

FRUIT SALAD (page 7)

Fruit seed: PIT

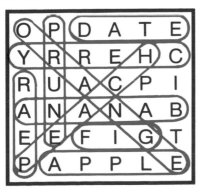

CROSSED WIRES (page 8)

Telephone pairs:

1 and 8	3 and 5
2 and 7	4 and 6

NAPPING NUMBERS (page 10)

A. 1, 3, 5, 7, **9**
B. 21, 16, 11, 6, **1**
C. 9, 11, 10, 12, 11, **13**
D. 1, 2, 4, 8, **16**
E. 5, 15, 25, 35, **45**
F. 4, 3, 4, 3, **4**

PUZZLE OF THE MONTH (page 11)

1. February has the fewest days.
2. March has a holiday with shamrocks and leprechauns.
3. January, June, and July all begin with "J."
4. Spring begins in March.
5. May has the fewest letters in its name.
6. September has the most letters in its name.
7. We celebrate Mother's Day and Memorial Day in May.
8. We celebrate Father's Day and Flag Day in June.
9. November has a holiday (Thanksgiving) that is always on a Thursday.
10. August comes after Independence Day and before Labor Day.

THE MYSTERY OF THE CASTLE (page 12)

My business is building castles of stone,
for kings, for queens, and for storing the throne.
My fun comes from hiding these words in the walls,
in a code that is carved in one of the halls.

LULU'S FIX-IT SHOP (page 15)

1. typewriter
2. television
3. hair dryer
4. washing machine
5. telephone
6. refrigerator
7. vacuum cleaner

LuLu is fixing a toaster.

MATCH THAT HAT (page 16)

DOT MAGIC (page 18)

CURIOUS CREATURES (page 20)

The Heedee is the pet from Yeldud

The Earth animals are:

Cassowary—a large, flightless bird from New Guinea with a bony crest called a casque

Saiga—a small, Asian goat with an enlarged snout

Ross's Turaco—an African bird with a waxy, yellow beak and a red "crew cut"

Coendu—a South American porcupine who can hang upside down by its tail

Red Uakari—a South American monkey with a bright red bald head and a short tail

Takin—a Chinese relative of the Musk Ox, with a big, round muzzle

Roseate Spoonbill—a Florida bird with pink feathers and a spoon-shaped beak

Pangolin—a scaly, ant-eating animal found in Asia and Africa

Spatulate-Nosed Tree Frog—a Central American frog

Markhor—a goat from Afghanistan with huge, spiral horns

Tarsier—a small primate from the Pacific Islands of Asia with huge eyes and a long tail

Jackson's Chameleon—an African chameleon who can change color and catch insects on its tongue

Babirusa—a wild pig from the East Indian Islands with huge tusks

INSTANT PICTURE (page 22)

GO FLY A KITE (page 23)

Flypaper

LOCKER LOGIC (page 24)

The lockers belong to: Ricky Camp, Susan Daniels, Pam O'Brien, Karen Smitty, and Donnie Zapley.

A SLIPPERY RIDDLE (page 26)

Banana peel

PICTURE CROSSWORD (page 27)

TWEETERS, PEEPERS, AND QUACKERS (page 28)

1. The sound a kitten makes is purr.
2. To frighten burglars, a dog will bark.
3. In the morning, a rooster will crow.
4. A mother hen will sometimes cluck.
5. Her baby chicks will follow with a peep.
6. A horse in a stable might neigh.
7. Cows in a barn are likely to moo.
8. Bees around flowers will often buzz.
9. A duck in a pond says quack.
10. A happy little bird may tweet.
11. A slinky snake likes to hiss.
12. In the jungle you'd hear a lion roar.
13. A frog in a pond would croak.

SQUEAKY'S SNEAKY SNACK (page 30)

MIXED-UP WARM-UPS (page 31)

1. hat—A
2. scarf—C
3. boots—B
4. mittens—F
5. earmuffs—D
6. leg warmers—E

DOT'S DEPARTMENT STORE (page 32)

ANIMALS, ANIMALS, ANIMALS (page 33)

SEA SIGHTS (page 34)

1. Starfish
2. Seahorse
3. Swordfish
4. Jellyfish
5. Dolphin

TOP IT OFF (page 35)

The large pizza is missing one olive slice.

PUZZLED POET (page 38)

As I looked upward toward the **sky**
I wondered with a longing **sigh**,
How things might look from way up **high**.
How would it feel if I could **fly**?

Do you think birds wonder, **too**,
As they're soaring in the **blue**
How it would be if they could **do**
People things like me and **you**?

SLICK SHIPPING COMPANY (page 39)

Fossil Order:
1. Triceratops
2. Allosaurus
3. Stegosaurus
4. Tyrannosaurus
5. Brontosaurus
6. Diplodocus
7. Birthday Cake (the box they slipped in)
8. Ankylosaurus

PLAY BALL! (page 40)

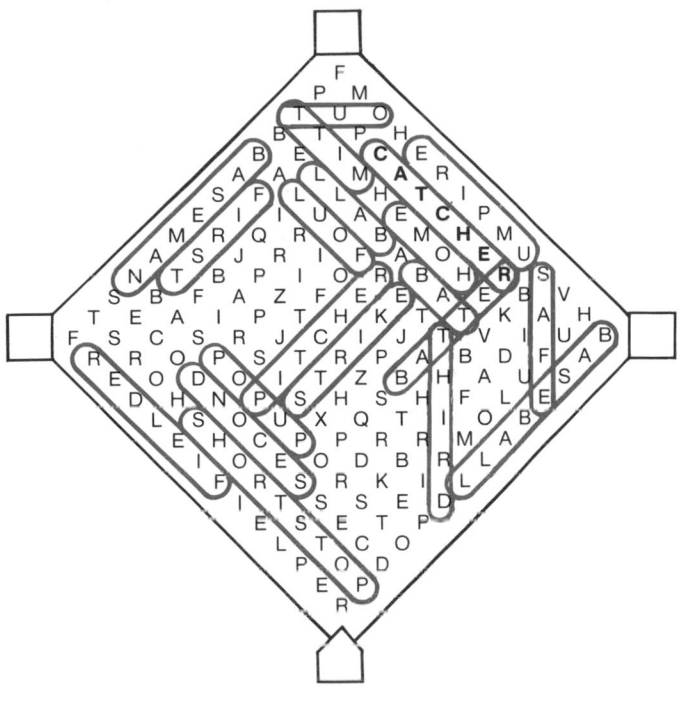

STOP, LOOK, AND LIST (page 42)

Foods	Colors	Girls' Names
Radish	Red	Rebecca
Toast	Tan	Tiffany
Waffle	White	Wendy
Grapes	Green	Gina
Butter	Blue	Beth

THE POTTER'S GIFT (page 43)

5.	4.
3.	1.
6.	2.

PICNIC MEMORIES (page 46)

1. Hamburgers and hot dogs were cooking on the grill.
2. Three people were playing horseshoes.
3. Four girls were playing volleyball.
4. The twins' names were Max and Marv.
5. Marty and Aunt Millie were playing checkers.
6. Three babies were at the picnic.
7. Munchkin the cat was under the picnic table.
8. Cousin Mark was balancing a picnic basket on his head.
9. The Munchlys have held their picnic for seven years.
10. Mrs. Munchly found a football in the cooler.

DOWNTOWN U.S.A. (page 46)

```
P H I L A D E L P H I A
    C H I C A G O
O R L A N D O
        C O L U M B U S
      L O S A N G E L E S
  A T L A N T A
  D E N V E R
```